FOLENS

IDEAS BANK

MATHEMATICS

Pattern

David Kirkby

Contents

Folens Publishers

How to use this book

Ideas Bank books provide you with ready to use, practical photocopiable activity sheets for your children, **plus** a wealth of ideas for extension and development.

TEACHER IDEAS PAGE　　　　**PHOTOCOPIABLE ACTIVITY SHEET**

Clear focus to the activity.

Answers given, with an explanation of the concept where relevant.

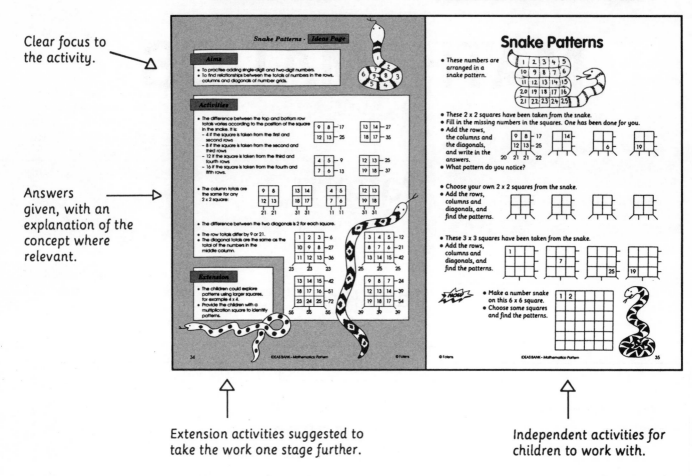

Extension activities suggested to take the work one stage further.

Independent activities for children to work with.

- Time saving, relevant and practical, **Ideas Bank** books ensure that you will always have work readily available.

Acknowledgements

Folens books are protected by International copyright laws. All rights reserved. The copyright of all materials in this book, except where otherwise stated, remains the property of the publisher and authors. No part of this publication may be reproduced, stored in a retrieval system, or transmitted, in any form or by any means, for whatever purpose, without the written permission of Folens Limited.

Folens do allow photocopying of selected pages of this publication for educational use, providing that this use is within the confines of the purchasing institution.

This resource may be used in a variety of ways; however, it is not intended that teachers or students should write into the book itself.

David Kirkby hereby asserts his moral right to be identified as the author of this work in accordance with the Copyright, Designs and Patents Act 1988.

© 1995 Folens Limited, on behalf of the author.

Editor: Angela Simms　　Cover by: In Touch Creative Services Ltd.　　Illustrations by: Cathy Gilligan　　Cover Photo by: The Image Bank.

First published 1995 by Folens Limited, Albert House, Apex Business Centre, Boscombe Road, Dunstable, LU5 4RL, England.

ISBN 185276794　　Printed in Singapore

Introduction

The nature of the resource

This book contains 22 activities on the theme of pattern. Each activity consists of a photocopiable activity sheet for classroom use, together with a page of teacher ideas to illustrate ways in which the activity sheet could be used.

Particular features of this book include:
- emphasis on the use of materials to support the children's learning
- fostering an investigational approach to learning mathematics
- the use of games as an integral part of the learning experience
- emphasis on the importance of display to support and extend the activities
- encouragement of the inclusion of mental mathematics within the activities.

The activity sheets

These are photocopiable and serve various purposes:
- Many sheets contain tables and diagrams to be completed by the children.
- Some sheets are designed as boards and score sheets to be used for mathematical games.
- Some sheets are pictures to be used in conjunction with other pieces of apparatus.
- Some sheets could be photocopied on to card, then cut up to produce sets of cards for the children to use in activities.

The activities

The book contains various activities that cover a range of learning experiences relating to pattern. Children should receive a varied 'diet' of mathematical activity. This particular 'diet' includes:
- games
- apparatus-based activities
- investigational activities
- practical activities.

The activities are not presented sequentially, leaving teachers the freedom to choose pages as appropriate. Each activity could be extended and varied in different ways. Some suggestions are made on each ideas page.

The ideas pages

These include comments and suggestions to help the teacher make full use of the activity sheets and develop specific activities. The pages include:
- the purpose of the activity
- descriptions of activities
- solutions where necessary
- rules for the games, with extension ideas and variations
- ideas for display
- extension ideas
- relevant mental activities.

Flower Patterns - Ideas Page

Aims

- To recognise and continue the patterns found in different number sequences (ascending and descending).
- To create and describe number sequences.

Activities

- The completed patterns and descriptions are:

counting numbers

odd numbers

even numbers

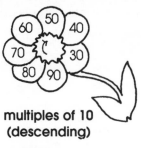

multiples of 10 (descending)

adding 4, starting at 5

subtracting 3, starting at 31

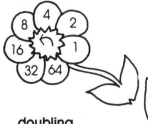

doubling (powers of 2)

adding 8, starting at 1

subtracting 6, starting at 52

Extension

- Expand the number sequences to include ten or twenty numbers.
- Vary the positions of the missing numbers:

- Introduce different sequences, such as the Fibonacci sequence. This starts with any two numbers and continues by adding the previous two numbers each time.

Display

- The activity page could be photocopied and enlarged with the numbers blanked out. The children could then design their own number sequences.

Fibonacci sequence						
1 **+** 2	3	5	8	13	21	...
4 **+** 2	6	8	14	22	36	...

Flower Patterns

- Follow the patterns on the petals of each flower.
- Write the correct number on each petal. Follow the arrows.

- Turn over and write a description of each pattern.
- Invent some of your own patterns.

Aims

- To investigate patterns in the sequence of units digits of multiples of different numbers.
- To search for relationships between different patterns.
- To recognise cyclic number sequences.

Display

- Illustrate the cyclic nature of the units digits for various times tables by drawing 'ten point' circles. Starting at zero, join the digits in the order in which they appear in the cycle.

x3 pattern

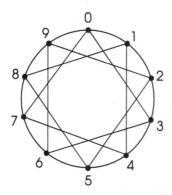

x4 pattern

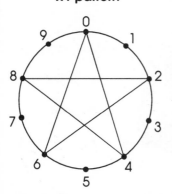

- Ask the children to draw 'ten point' circles for other times tables.

Activities

- Calculators could be used to make the activity accessible to lower-ability children.
- The units digit patterns are shown in the table:

  (The repeating cycles of numbers have been highlighted.)

  x 4 : **4 8 2 6 0** 4 8 2 6 0 4 8
  x 3 : **3 6 9 2 5 8 1 4 7 0** 3 6
  x 8 : **8 6 4 2 0** 8 6 4 2 0 8 6

- The patterns for the four-times and eight-times tables are similar, repeating the same set of five digits. The table could be extended to show the ten-digit cycle for the three-times table.
- The cycles for the other times tables up to nine are:

  (The repeating cycles of numbers have been highlighted.)

  x 2 : **2 4 6 8 0** 2 4 6 8 0 2 4
  x 5 : **5 0** 5 0 5 0 5 0 5 0 5 0
  x 6 : **6 2 8 4 0** 6 2 8 4 0 6 2
  x 7 : **7 4 1 8 5 2 9 6 3 0** 7 4
  x 9 : **9 8 7 6 5 4 3 2 1 0** 9 8

- Draw the children's attention to:
  - the interesting decreasing pattern in the nine-times table
  - the one-times table, which is the reverse of the nine-times table
  - the three-times table, which is the reverse of the seven-times table and contains a ten-digit cycle
  - the same set of repeating digits in the four-, eight-, two- and six-times tables.

Extension

- Explore the patterns of the units digits for times tables beyond nine.

IDEAS BANK – *Mathematics: Pattern*

© Folens

Units Patterns

Complete the four-times table.

- Write the units digit of each number in the table.
- What pattern do these numbers make?

			Units
1 x 4 =	4	4
2 x 4 =	8	8
3 x 4 =	12	2
4 x 4 =	16	6
5 x 4 =	20	0
6 x 4 =		
7 x 4 =		
8 x 4 =		
9 x 4 =		
10 x 4 =		

- Complete these tables in the same way.

			Units
1 x 3 =	3	3
2 x 3 =	6	6
3 x 3 =		
4 x 3 =		
5 x 3 =		
6 x 3 =		
7 x 3 =		
8 x 3 =		
9 x 3 =		
10 x 3 =		

			Units
1 x 8 =		
2 x 8 =		
3 x 8 =		
4 x 8 =		
5 x 8 =		
6 x 8 =		
7 x 8 =		
8 x 8 =		
9 x 8 =		
10 x 8 =		

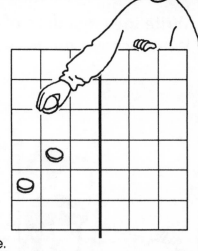

Aims

- To draw the reflections of patterns using a mirror line.

Display

- Collect and display sets of different symmetrical patterns on a 4 x 4 square grid.
- Display patterns which have a horizontal line of symmetry:

Activities

- Ask the children to create symmetrical patterns by positioning counters on a square grid.
- Introduce a mirror line. Organise the class into pairs. Draw a large 6 x 6 square with a mirror line. One child places a set of counters on one side of the line, then the second child positions the same number of counters symmetrically on the other side.
- Lower-ability children could use mirrors to check lines of symmetry, particularly diagonal lines.

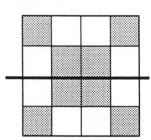 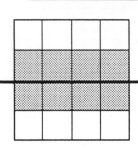 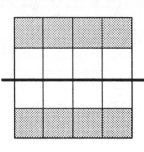 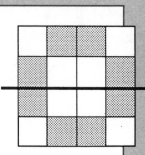

- Draw patterns with other lines of symmetry, such as:

- Ask the children to identify patterns constructed with one mirror line that have two lines of symmetry, such as:

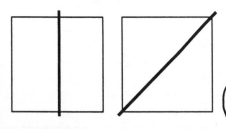

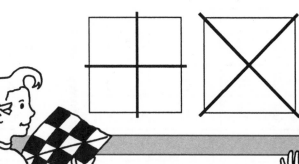

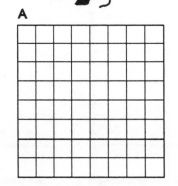

Extension

- Use large square grids (as in **A**) or non-square grids (as in **B**) as shown.
- The children could look for and draw some symmetrical patterns that they find in the environment, for example wallpaper or carpet patterns.

A

B

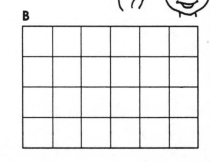

IDEAS BANK– *Mathematics: Pattern*

Symmetry Patterns

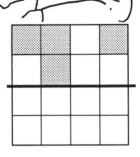

- Colour the squares on the other side of the mirror line to make the patterns symmetrical.

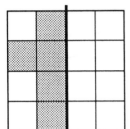 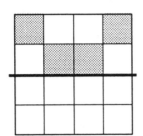 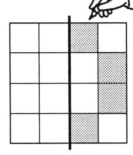 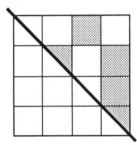

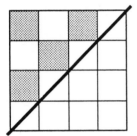 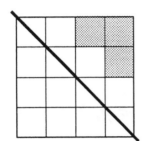 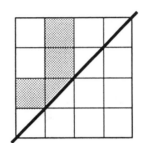 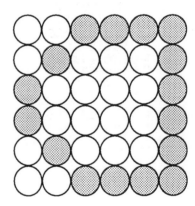

- Draw the mirror lines on these symmetrical patterns.

 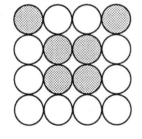 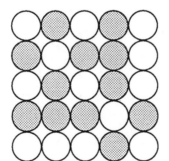 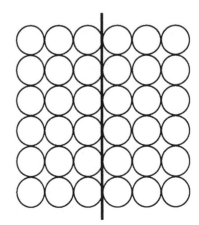

 • Design your own symmetrical patterns.

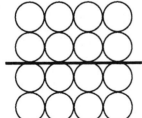 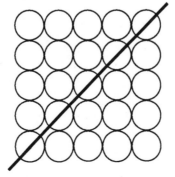

Odd and Even Patterns - Ideas Page

Aims

- To investigate patterns which result from the addition of odd and even numbers.

Activities

- The first activity results in odd numbers; the second and third in even numbers. These activities aim to help the children to recognise the following relationships:

+	odd	even
odd	even	odd
even	odd	even

- Subtraction leads to a similar pattern.

-	odd	even
odd	even	odd
even	odd	even

Display

- The children could construct an addition square for the numbers one to ten. The numbers could then be highlighted to illustrate each pattern. This square highlights the pattern which results from the addition of odd numbers.

+	1	2	3	4	5	6	7	8	9	10
1	2	3	4	5	6	7	8	9	10	11
2	3	4	5	6	7	8	9	10	11	12
3	4	5	6	7	8	9	10	11	12	13
4	5	6	7	8	9	10	11	12	13	14
5	6	7	8	9	10	11	12	13	14	15
6	7	8	9	10	11	12	13	14	15	16
7	8	9	10	11	12	13	14	15	16	17
8	9	10	11	12	13	14	15	16	17	18
9	10	11	12	13	14	15	16	17	18	19
10	11	12	13	14	15	16	17	18	19	20

Extension

- Ask the children to repeat the activity, this time multiplying the numbers. The answers result in the pattern shown below.

X	odd	even
odd	even	odd
even	odd	even

- Reinforce the pattern by drawing a multiplication square. This square highlights the pattern formed by the multiplication of odd numbers.

X	1	2	3	4	5	6	7	8	9	10
1	1	2	3	4	5	6	7	8	9	10
2	2	4	6	8	10	12	14	16	18	20
3	3	6	9	12	15	18	21	24	27	30
4	4	8	12	16	20	24	28	32	36	40
5	5	10	15	20	25	30	35	40	45	50
6	6	12	18	24	30	36	42	48	54	60
7	7	14	21	28	35	42	49	56	63	70
8	8	16	24	32	40	48	56	64	72	80
9	9	18	27	36	45	54	63	72	81	90
10	10	20	30	40	50	60	70	80	90	100

Odd and Even Patterns

Odd Numbers   **Even Numbers**

- Choose one odd number and one even number.
- Add your numbers and write the answers.

1. __3__ + __12__ = __15__   2. ___ + ___ = ___   3. ___ + ___ = ___

4. ___ + ___ = ___   5. ___ + ___ = ___

- Are the answers odd or even numbers? _____

- Choose two odd numbers from the boxes.
- Add your numbers and write the answers.

1. __5__ + __19__ = __24__   2. ___ + ___ = ___   3. ___ + ___ = ___

4. ___ + ___ = ___   5. ___ + ___ = ___

- Are the answers odd or even numbers? _____

- Choose two even numbers from the boxes.
- Add your numbers and write the answers.

1. __18__ + __8__ = __26__   2. ___ + ___ = ___   3. ___ + ___ = ___

4. ___ + ___ = ___   5. ___ + ___ = ___

- Are the answers odd or even numbers? _____

- Turn over and write about the patterns you have found.
- Repeat the activity, this time subtracting the numbers.

Shape Patterns - Ideas Page

Aims

- To make patterns by drawing the diagonals of regular pentagons and hexagons, and colouring the regions that are created.
- To explore the rotational properties of these patterns.

Activities

- Encourage the children to construct further patterns. Provide them with regular pentagonal and hexagonal templates to draw around. They should then draw in all the diagonals which will form the basis of their pattern.

- A pentagram pattern that is created within a pentagon:

- Many patterns could be drawn with hexagonal templates, such as:

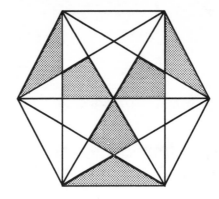

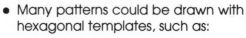

- Identify and discuss the shapes that are created within the hexagon. For example, point out the two overlapping equilateral triangles in the first hexagon in the final activity.

Display

- Display examples of the children's patterns. Some of the designs could be cut out to create patterned five-pointed and six-pointed stars.
- The children could investigate the rotational symmetry of their patterns. Ask them to cut out a pattern and find out what happens to the pattern when it is rotated.

Extension

- Ask the children to draw and count the number of diagonals in a pentagon, a hexagon, and other polygons. How many regions are created within each shape when the diagonals are drawn in?
- Further activities could include:
  - creating patterns based on drawing the diagonals of different regular polygons, such as a square, octagon, decagon
  - searching for examples of these patterns in the

Shape Patterns

Create your own patterns in these pentagons.

- Draw the diagonals first, then create your patterns. You may need to draw some extra lines to help you, as shown in the second pattern.

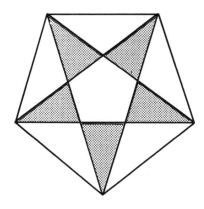 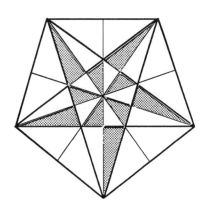 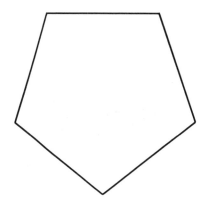

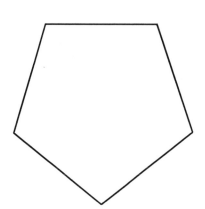 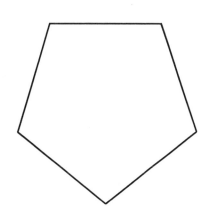 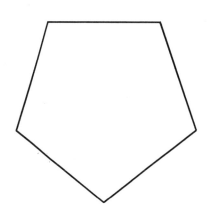

- Create some patterns using these hexagons.

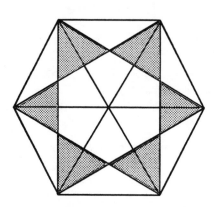 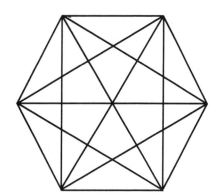 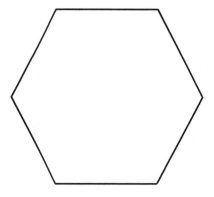

 • Draw another shape. Draw its diagonals and make a pattern.

Aims

- To reinforce knowledge of the area and perimeter of rectangles.
- To consider relationships between area and perimeter.
- To search for and describe patterns using a table grid.

Display

- The children could draw and complete an area and a perimeter table. Draw their attention to the fact that the area table is the same as a multiplication table.

Area

Width of rectangle

	1	2	3	4	5	6	7	8
1	1	2	3	4	5	6	7	8
2	2	4	6	8	10	12	14	16
3	3	6	9	12	15	18	21	24
4	4	8	12	16	20	24	28	32
5	5	10	15	20	25	30	35	40
6	6	12	18	24	30	36	42	48
7	7	14	21	28	35	42	49	56
8	8	16	24	32	40	48	56	64

Length of rectangle

Perimeter

Width of rectangle

	1	2	3	4	5	6	7	8
1	4	6	8	10	12	14	16	18
2	6	8	10	12	14	16	18	20
3	8	10	12	14	16	18	20	22
4	10	12	14	16	18	20	22	24
5	12	14	16	18	20	22	24	26
6	14	16	18	20	22	24	26	28
7	16	18	20	22	24	26	28	30
8	18	20	22	24	26	28	30	32

Length of rectangle

Activities

- The answers for the first section are:

Area	= 15 units
Perimeter	= 16 units
Difference	= 1 unit

Area	= 6 units
Perimeter	= 10 units
Difference	= 4 units

Area	= 8 units
Perimeter	= 12 units
Difference	= 4 units

- When the children have drawn all of the rectangles and made all of the calculations, the completed table should look like this:

Width of rectangle

	1	2	3	4	5	6	7	8
1	3	4	5	6	7	8	9	10
2	4	4	4	4	4	4	4	4
3	5	4	3	2	1	0	1	2
4	6	4	2	0	2	4	6	8
5	7	4	1	2	5	8	11	14
6	8	4	0	4	8	12	16	20
7	9	4	1	6	11	16	21	26
8	10	4	2	8	14	20	26	32

Length of rectangle

- Discuss the number patterns that appear in the table:
  - the symmetrical pattern about the diagonal
  - the sequential patterns along each row and down each column
  - the concentration of fours in the second row and second column.
- Ask the children to locate the zeros in the table and find out what they mean.

- Ask the children to draw rectangles which have the same area but different dimensions. They should label the perimeter of each. Similarly, rectangles with the same perimeter but different areas could be drawn, labelled and displayed.

Area and Perimeter Patterns

- For each of these rectangles, find:
  - the area
  - the perimeter
  - the difference between these two numbers.

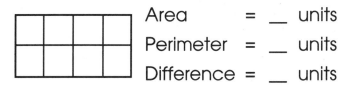

Area = __ units
Perimeter = __ units
Difference = __ units

Area = __ units
Perimeter = __ units
Difference = __ units

Area = __ units
Perimeter = __ units
Difference = __ units

- Write the differences in the table below.
  One has been done for you.
- Complete the table. You will need to :
  - draw different-sized rectangles on squared paper
  - find the differences between the area and the perimeter for these rectangles, and write the answers in the table.

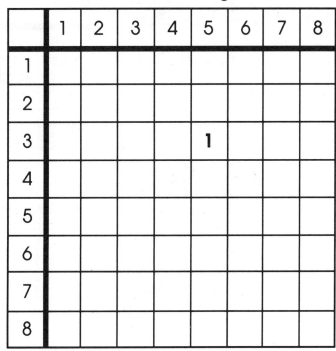

Width of rectangle

	1	2	3	4	5	6	7	8
1								
2								
3				1				
4								
5								
6								
7								
8								

Length of rectangle

Aims

- To investigate the number of arrangements of a fixed set of colours.
- To develop a systematic approach to problem-solving.

Activities

- The combinations for the first activity are shown here.
- The children could use coloured cubes to create the different trains before they begin to shade.
- Encourage the children to approach the problem systematically. For example, if the first colour is red, what could the other colours be? When these arrangements have been found, they could identify the number of different colour combinations if the first carriage was green.

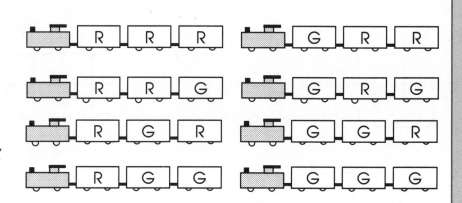

- The colour combinations for the second activity are shown below.
- Encourage the children to apply the method that they used for the first part of the activity. They should work out the combinations when the first colour is yellow, then blue, and finally pink.
- There are sixteen different colour combinations for the final activity (four carriages, two colours):

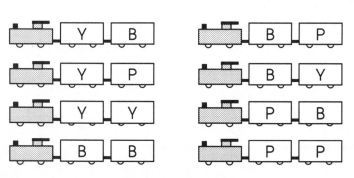

OOOO	OOOP	OOPO	OOPP
OPOO	OPPO	OPOP	OPPP
POOO	POOP	POPO	POPP
PPOO	PPOP	PPPO	PPPP

Extension

- Ask the children to investigate different ways of shading this flag using two colours.
- They could then find different ways of shading this three-storey block using two colours. The towers could be built using interlocking cubes.

Display

- The children could create and display the colour combinations using interlocking cubes.

Train Patterns

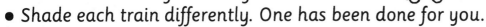

- Make each carriage red or green.
- Shade each train differently. One has been done for you.

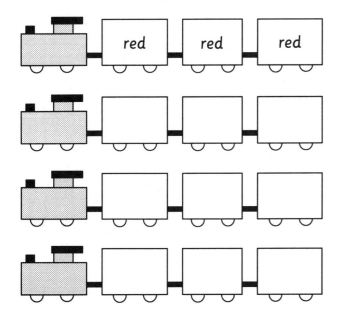

| red | red | red |

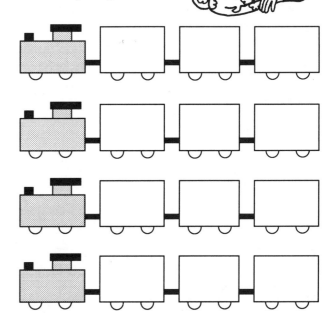

- Make each carriage yellow, blue or pink.
- Shade each train differently. One has been done for you.

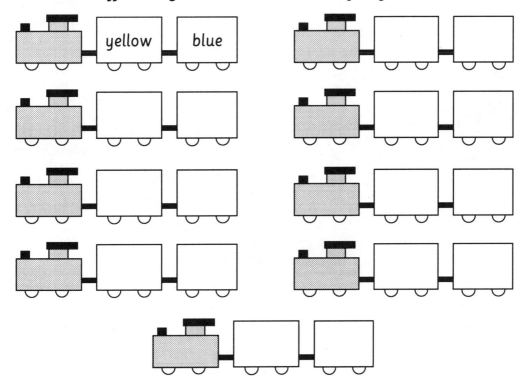

| yellow | blue |

- Draw a train with four carriages.
  You could make these orange and purple.
- How many different ways could you shade the train?

Tables Patterns - Ideas Page

Aims

- To explore the number patterns in the 10 x 10 multiplication square.
- To investigate numbers which are multiples of several numbers (those that appear in several times tables).
- To introduce prime numbers.

Activities

- The numbers that appear:
  - three times are 4, 9, 16, 36
  - four times are 12, 20, 24, 30, 40.
- The eighteen numbers that do not appear at all are:

11	13	17	19	23	26	29	31	33
34	37	38	39	41	43	44	46	47

- The children could extend the table beyond ten to find out:
  - which of the eighteen missing numbers will appear (26, 33, 34, 38, 39, 44, 46)
  - which numbers will never appear (11, 13, 17, 19, 23, 29, 31, 37, 41, 43, 47). These are the prime numbers below 50.

Display

- An enlarged version of the multiplication square could be displayed. Encourage the children to identify number patterns, for example the:
  - pattern in the ninth row
  - pattern in the fifth column
  - symmetrical pattern about the diagonal
  - pattern in the numbers along the diagonal (square numbers).
- The children could use these patterns to practise their times tables. For example, ask them to recite the sixth column, or the third row, without looking. They could then check their answers.

The digital root of 56 is...

$5 + 6 = 11$

$1 + 1 = 2$

...2

Extension

- The children could extend the table by an extra five rows and five columns. Ask them to investigate whether any other numbers appear several times.
- Explain how to find the digital root of a number. Continue to add the digits of a number until a single-digit number is obtained. For example, the digital root of 56 is 2 because $5 + 6 = 11$, then $1 + 1 = 2$. Therefore, the digital roots of the multiples of 3 are: 3, 6, 9, 3, 6, 9, 3, 6, 9, and so on. Ask the children to find the digital roots of the numbers in the table and to identify any number patterns.

Tables Patterns

- Check the four-times table by looking down the fourth column or along the fourth row.
- Check other times tables in the same way.

1	2	3	4	5	6	7	8	9	10
2	4	6	8	10	12	14	16	18	20
3	6	9	12	15	18	21	24	27	30
4	8	12	16	20	24	28	32	36	40
5	10	15	20	25	30	35	40	45	50
6	12	18	24	30	36	42	48	54	60
7	14	21	28	35	42	49	56	63	70
8	16	24	32	40	48	56	64	72	80
9	18	27	36	45	54	63	72	81	90
10	20	30	40	50	60	70	80	90	100

- Look carefully at the table and write down the numbers that appear:

  - three times _____

  - four times _____

- There are eighteen numbers up to 50 which do not appear at all.
- Find these numbers and write them in this table.

IDEAS BANK – *Mathematics: Pattern*

Aims

- To investigate different arrangements based on facial features.
- To encourage a systematic approach to problem-solving.
- To reinforce the children's knowledge of fractions.

Activities

- The arrangements of facial features for the first part of the activity are:

- Develop the activity by asking the children to:
  - point to a face and describe it
  - identify a face from a verbal description
  - count the number of sad faces
  - count the number of happy faces
  - count the number of faces that are looking left and have triangular noses, and so on.

- The arrangements for the second part of the activity are:

Display

- Provide the children with card circles. They could use these to draw or paint faces. Encourage them to add other elements, such as paper hats. The work could be mounted and displayed in the classroom.
- A display of faces with differing characteristics could be changed regularly and used to reinforce work on fractions.

Extension

- Use the patterns for basic fraction work. What proportion of the faces do the children think are:
  - happy or sad?
  - happy and looking left?
  - sad and looking left?
  - happy, looking left and have square noses?
  - neither happy nor looking left?
  To begin with, ask the children to identify only halves, quarters and eighths.

IDEAS BANK – *Mathematics: Pattern*

Face Patterns

- Faces can be   – happy or sad

  – looking left or looking right

  – with a triangular nose or a square nose.

- Draw seven different faces.

- Faces can be   – happy, sad or in-between

  – looking up or looking down

  – wearing or not wearing a hat.

- Draw eleven different faces.

- The next set of faces can be round, square or triangular, and happy or sad.
- How many different faces can you draw?

Aims

- To investigate the patterns formed when consecutive numbers are added.
- To use patterns to solve addition problems.

Extension

- Ask the children to identify numbers that cannot be expressed as the sum of consecutive numbers, such as 1, 2, 4, 8 and 16, and to identify the pattern formed.
- Ask them to find examples of numbers that can be expressed in several ways.
- The children could find out whether all numbers can be expressed as the sum of consecutive numbers. Ask them to draw and complete a table like the one below.

Activities

- When the sets of two consecutive numbers are added the answers are:

  3, 5, 7, 9, 11, 13, 15, 17, 19, 21 (**odd numbers**)

- Point out that any odd number (except 1) can be expressed as the sum of two consecutive numbers.
- When the sets of three consecutive numbers are added the answers are:

  6, 9, 12, 15, 18, 21, 24, 27, 30, 33 (**multiples of 3**)

- Emphasise that any multiples of 3 (except 3) can be expressed as the sum of three consecutive numbers. Also, the middle number is always one third of the sum.
- When the sets of four consecutive numbers are added the answers are:

  10, 14, 18, 22, 26, 30, 34 (**increasing by 4 each time**)

- Draw the children's attention to the fact that these are multiples of 2 (except 2), but are not multiples of 4. Also, when these numbers are divided by 2 the answer is an odd number.

1		11	5 + 6	
2		12	3 + 4 + 5	
3	1 + 2	13	6 + 7	
4		14	2 + 3 + 4 + 5	
5	2 + 3	15	7 + 8 4 + 5 + 6 1 + 2 + 3 + 4 + 5	
6	1 + 2 + 3	16		
7	3 + 4	17	8 + 9	
8		18	5 + 6 + 7 3 + 4 + 5 + 6	
9	4 + 5 2 + 3 + 4	19	9 + 10	
10	1 + 2 + 3 + 4	20	2 + 3 + 4 + 5 + 6	

Display

- Numbers that can be expressed in several ways could be illustrated by strips of coloured paper (coloured according to length) or number rods.

Consecutive Patterns

- Add these sets of two consecutive numbers:

$1 + 2 =$ _____

$2 + 3 =$ _____

$3 + 4 =$ _____

$4 + 5 =$ _____

$5 + 6 =$ _____

$6 + 7 =$ _____

$7 + 8 =$ _____

$8 + 9 =$ _____

$9 + 10 =$ _____

$10 + 11 =$ _____

- What do you notice about the answers?

_____

- Add these sets of three consecutive numbers:

$1 + 2 + 3 =$ _____

$2 + 3 + 4 =$ _____

$3 + 4 + 5 =$ _____

$4 + 5 + 6 =$ _____

$5 + 6 + 7 =$ _____

$6 + 7 + 8 =$ _____

$7 + 8 + 9 =$ _____

$8 + 9 + 10 =$ _____

$9 + 10 + 11 =$ _____

$10 + 11 + 12 =$ _____

- What do you notice about the answers?

_____

- Fill in the missing consecutive numbers.

___ + ___ = 25

___ + ___ = 51

___ + ___ = 37

___ + ___ = 41

- Fill in the missing consecutive numbers.

___ + ___ + ___ = 39

___ + ___ + ___ = 90

___ + ___ + ___ = 60

___ + ___ + ___ = 54

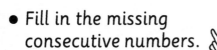

- Add sets of four consecutive numbers.

Aims

- To create patterns by joining patterned tiles together.
- To recognise the symmetry of a pattern.

Extension

- Ask the children to experiment with tiles which incorporate curved lines:

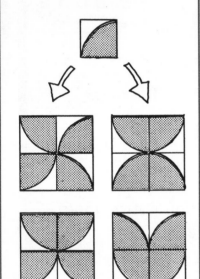

Activities

- Some examples of two-tile patterns:

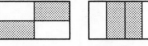

- Some examples of four-tile patterns:

- Encourage the children to create more complex tiles by using combinations of the tiles shown above. For example:

Display

- Use the patterns for work on symmetry. Ask the children to sort and classify the tiles they have drawn according to the number of lines of symmetry. The different categories could then be labelled and displayed:

Lines of symmetry

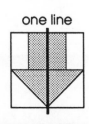
one line

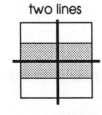
two lines

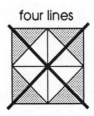
four lines

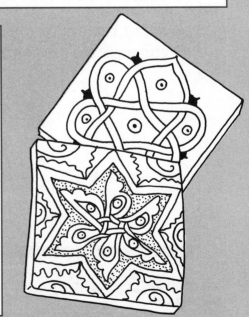

Tiling Patterns

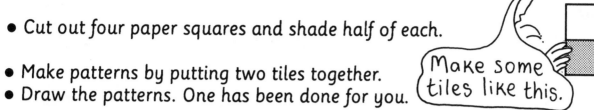

- Cut out four paper squares and shade half of each.

- Make patterns by putting two tiles together.
- Draw the patterns. One has been done for you.

Make some tiles like this.

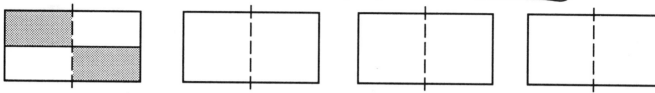

- Make patterns by putting four tiles together. Draw them below.
  One has been done for you.

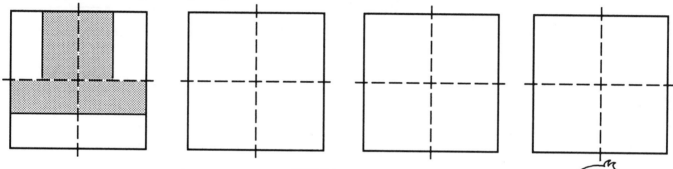

- Make some new tiles like this:

- Draw the patterns here.

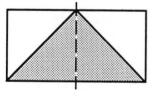 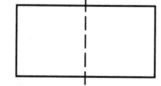 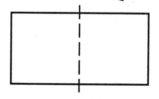 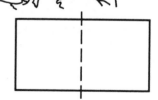

- Make patterns by putting four tiles together. Draw them below.

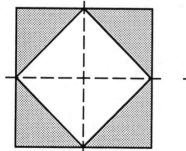 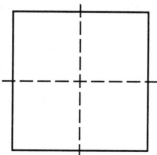 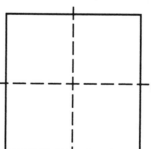 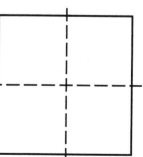

- Invent your own tiles and make patterns with them.

Spot Patterns - Ideas Page

Aims

- To reinforce the children's knowledge of multiplication by counting groups of objects.
- To learn multiplication facts.
- To introduce the idea of factor pairs of a number.

Extension

- Encourage the children to experiment with the rectangles they have already made to find out how many spots could be used to create:
  - two different rectangles
  - three different rectangles
  - four different rectangles.

  Point out that prime numbers of spots can be used to create only one type of rectangle.
- Discuss the similarities between, for example, the 3 x 5 and 5 x 3 rectangles. This is the **commutative** property of multiplication.

Activities

- The completed table is:

Shape	Number of row spots	Number of column spots	Total spots
A	2	7	14
B	5	2	10
C	3	3	9
D	3	6	18
E	3	2	6
F	7	4	28

- The children could use counters to create rectangular patterns. Pegs and pegboards are even better.
- They could make the following rectangles with:
  - sixteen spots, 1 x 16, 2 x 8, 4 x 4
  - fifteen spots, 1 x 15, 3 x 5
  - twenty-four spots, 1 x 24, 2 x 12, 3 x 8, 4 x 6
  - eighteen spots, 1 x 18, 2 x 9, 3 x 6.

Display

- Draw and display a multiplication square. This could be used to discuss the different properties of the rectangles.

Row spots

1	2	3	4	5	6	7	8	9	10
2	4	6	8	10	12	14	16	18	20
3	6	9	12	15	18	21	24	27	30
4	8	12	16	20	24	28	32	36	40
5	10	15	20	25	30	35	40	45	50
6	12	18	24	30	36	42	48	54	60
7	14	21	28	35	42	49	56	63	70
8	16	24	32	40	48	56	64	72	80
9	18	27	36	45	54	63	72	81	90
10	20	30	40	50	60	70	80	90	100

Column spots

- Ask the children to make different displays for given numbers of spots. Self-adhesive coloured 'spot' labels are ideal for this.

24 spot pattern

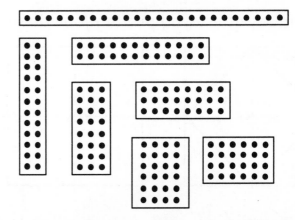

Spot Patterns

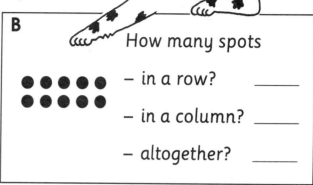

• Find the answers. One has been done for you.

A

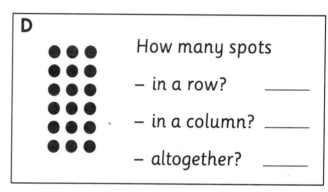

How many spots

– in a row? _2_

– in a column? _7_

– altogether? _14_

B

How many spots

– in a row? _____

– in a column? _____

– altogether? _____

C

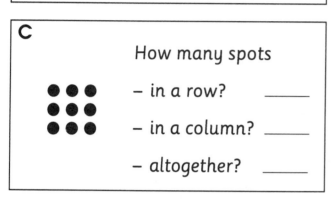

How many spots

– in a row? _____

– in a column? _____

– altogether? _____

D

How many spots

– in a row? _____

– in a column? _____

– altogether? _____

E

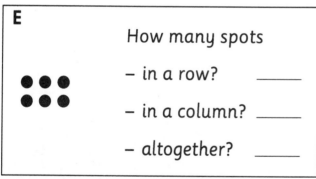

How many spots

– in a row? _____

– in a column? _____

– altogether? _____

F

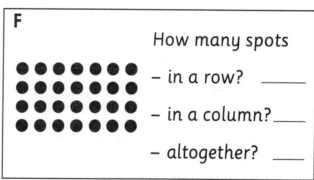

How many spots

– in a row? _____

– in a column? _____

– altogether? _____

• Complete this table.
• Use counters to make as many rectangles as you can with these total numbers of spots: 16, 15, 24, 18.

Shape	Number of row spots	Number of column spots	Total spots
A			
B			
C			
D			
E			
F			

Sequence Patterns - Ideas Page

Aims

- To recognise and complete different number sequences.
- To describe number patterns.
- To create number sequences.

Activities

- The completed patterns and descriptions are:

1	3	5	7	9	11	13	15	(odd numbers)
3	6	9	12	15	18	21	24	(multiples of 3)
2	4	6	8	10	12	14	16	(even numbers)
5	10	15	20	25	30	35	40	(multiples of 5)
1	4	9	16	25	36	49	64	(square numbers)

- Provide the children with copies of the activity sheet with the numbers blanked out. The children could create their own sequences, first using a number line, then transferring their answers to their copy of the activity sheet.

Extension

- Ask the children to create sequence patterns for all the multiples in order, such as:

  - **multiples of 2**:
    2, 4, 6, 8, 10 ...

  - **multiples of 3**:
    3, 6, 9, 12, 15 ...

  - **multiples of 4**:
    4, 8, 12, 16, 20 ...

- These patterns could be used in a multiplication square.

Display

- Make a 'washing line' by positioning clothes pegs at regular intervals along a cord suspended in the classroom. The children could make a set of numbered cards and 'hang out' a number sequence on the line.

- Use the 'washing line' to focus on particular properties of the sequence and to set different challenges. For example:

  - Ask the children to follow the sequence and hang out the remaining numbers to dry.

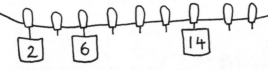

  - Ask them to hang out the missing numbers in the sequence.

Sequence Patterns

- Find the patterns in these sequences.
- Write in the missing numbers.
- Write a description of the pattern in the box.

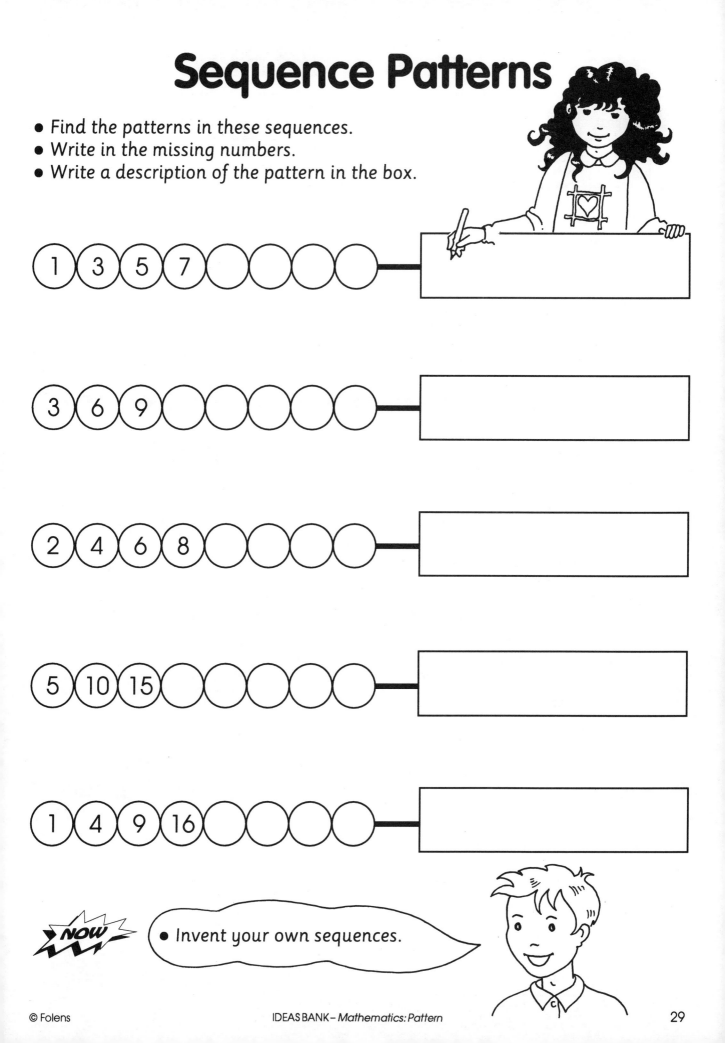

(1)(3)(5)(7)( )( )( )( )

(3)(6)(9)( )( )( )( )( )

(2)(4)(6)(8)( )( )( )( )

(5)(10)(15)( )( )( )( )( )

(1)(4)(9)(16)( )( )( )( )

NOW • Invent your own sequences.

Reversing Patterns - Ideas Page

Aims

- To explore and describe the patterns in the digits of two-digit numbers.
- To practise subtracting one two-digit number from another.

Activities

- The answers for the first set of subtractions are all 18. The answers for the second set are all 36.
- The two-digit numbers for the sets of subtractions have a common factor. The first set all have digits that differ by 2 and the second set have digits that differ by 4.
- The children could choose two-digit numbers with the same difference between the digits. Ask them to reverse and subtract the digits to see whether any patterns emerge. For example:

  – digit difference of 1 — numbers = 12, 23, 34, 45 ... subtraction = 9
  – digit difference of 3 — numbers = 14, 25, 36, 47 ... subtraction = 27

Extension

- The children could repeat the activity, using three-digit numbers. Some children may need to use calculators. Ask them to investigate patterns in the middle digits and in the two other digits.

$$
\begin{array}{ccc}
721 & 542 & 863 \\
127 & 245 & 368 \\
\hline
594 & 297 & 495
\end{array}
$$

- Ask the children to reverse the digits of the answer and add the new number to the original answer. For example:

$$
\begin{array}{ccc}
721 & 542 & 863 \\
127 & 245 & 368 \\
\hline
594 & 297 & 495 \\
+595 & 792 & 594 \\
\hline
1089 & 1089 & 1089
\end{array}
$$

- They could reverse and add two-digit numbers. Sometimes **palindromic** numbers are produced. For example:

$$
\begin{array}{ccc}
31 & 53 & 51 \\
13 & 35 & 15 \\
\hline
44 & 88 & 66
\end{array}
$$

If the first sum does not result in a palindromic number, the children should continue the process.

Display

- Ask the children to make a large 1–100 square and shade the numbers based on their digit difference when reversed. For example, they could shade blue the numbers with a digit difference of one (such as 12 and 23), and then look for patterns in the shaded numbers.

Reversing Patterns

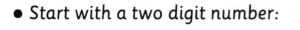

- Start with a two digit number: 31

- Reverse the digits: 13

- Subtract the numbers to find the difference: (18)

- Do the same with these numbers:

53	75	42	64

Reverse _____ _____ _____ _____

Subtract ⬭ ⬭ ⬭ ⬭

62	84	51	95

Reverse _____ _____ _____ _____

Subtract ⬭ ⬭ ⬭ ⬭

- Do you notice any pattern?

- Choose your own two-digit numbers.
- Reverse them and find the differences.

Spiral Patterns - Ideas Page

Aims

- To investigate patterns created by a repeating sequence of moves on a grid.
- To search for relationships between the three digits which determine the length and order of movement, and the resulting pattern.
- To consolidate ideas of rotational symmetry.

Extension

- The children could construct patterns using different numbers, for example: 2, 10, 3.
- Introduce patterns created by a sequence of four digits, using a triangular (isometric) dotty grid. Instead of turning right (a right-angle turn), the movement requires a 60 degree clockwise turn.
  Here is an example of a 1, 2, 3, 4 pattern:

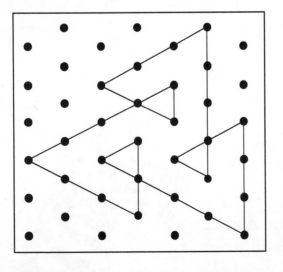

Activities

- The two exercises produce 'windmill' patterns:

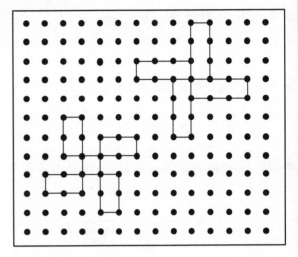

- When the children begin to produce their own spirals, advise them to choose smaller numbers. This will ensure that the pattern fits on to the grid.
- Discuss the activity to help the children recognise the relationship between the numbers they have chosen and the resulting patterns. For example, ask them to investigate if sets of three numbers always produce a 'windmill' pattern.

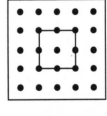 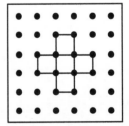

Display

- Patterns could be displayed according to type and in different colours, for example:

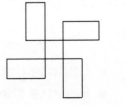

2, 1, 4

Spiral Patterns

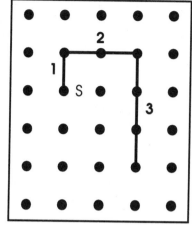

- Choose three digits between 1 and 5.
- Make a spiral pattern. Mark a starting dot S. Draw a line to match the first digit (such as 1).
- Now turn right. Draw a line to match the second digit (such as 2).
- Turn right again. Draw a line to match the third digit (such as 3).
- Repeat the sequence. For example, turn right 1 unit, then right 2 units, and so on.
- Continue until you return to S.
- Make spiral patterns on this grid with these digits:
  - 2, 1, 4
  - 1, 3, 4

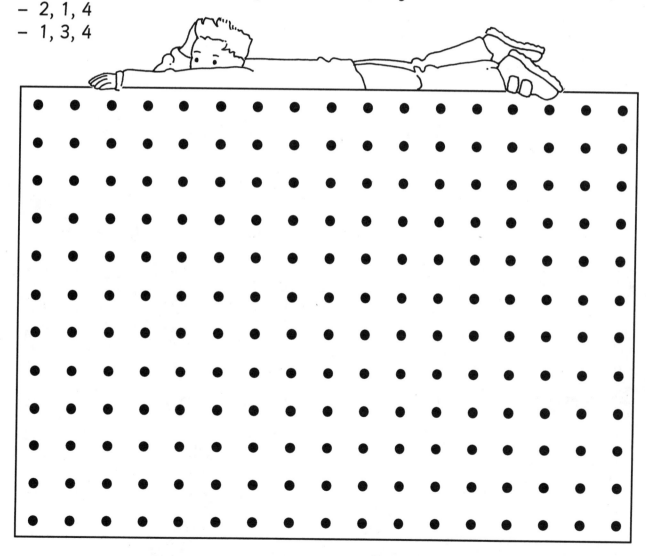

- Use squared paper to make your own spirals.
- Do they all result in the same pattern?

Snake Patterns - Ideas Page

Aims

- To practise adding single-digit and two-digit numbers.
- To find relationships between the totals of numbers in the rows, columns and diagonals of number grids.

Activities

- The difference between the top and bottom row totals varies according to the position of the square in the snake. It is:
  - 4 if the square is taken from the first and second rows
  - 8 if the square is taken from the second and third rows
  - 12 if the square is taken from the third and fourth rows
  - 16 if the square is taken from the fourth and fifth rows.

9	8	— 17
12	13	— 25

13	14	— 27
18	17	— 35

4	5	— 9
7	6	— 13

12	13	— 25
19	18	— 37

- The column totals are the same for any 2 x 2 square:

9	8
12	13
21	21

13	14
18	17
31	31

4	5
7	6
11	11

12	13
19	18
31	31

- The difference between the two diagonals is 2 for each square.

- The row totals differ by 9 or 21.
- The diagonal totals are the same as the total of the numbers in the middle column.

1	2	3	— 6
10	9	8	— 27
11	12	13	— 36
23	23	23	

3	4	5	— 12
8	7	6	— 21
13	14	15	— 42
25	25	25	

Extension

- The children could explore patterns using larger squares, for example 4 x 4.
- Provide the children with a multiplication square to identify patterns.

13	14	15	— 42
18	17	16	— 51
23	24	25	— 72
55	55	55	

9	8	7	— 24
12	13	14	— 39
19	18	17	— 54
39	39	39	

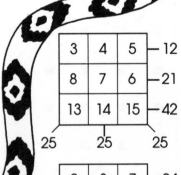

Snake Patterns

- These numbers are arranged in a snake pattern.

- These 2 x 2 squares have been taken from the snake.
- Fill in the missing numbers in the squares. One has been done for you.
- Add the rows, the columns and the diagonals, and write in the answers.

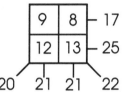

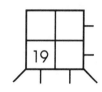

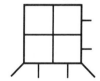

- What pattern do you notice?

- Choose your own 2 x 2 squares from the snake.
- Add the rows, columns and diagonals, and find the patterns.

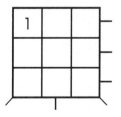

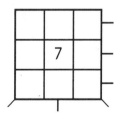

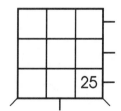

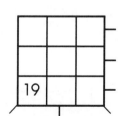

- These 3 x 3 squares have been taken from the snake.
- Add the rows, columns and diagonals, and find the patterns.

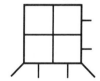

- Make a number snake on this 6 x 6 square.
- Choose some squares and find the patterns.

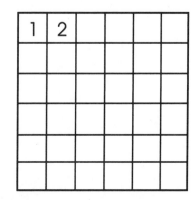

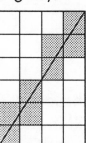

Diagonal Patterns - Ideas Page

Aims

- To identify the relationship between the diagonals of rectangles and their dimensions.
- To approach a problem systematically.

Extension

- Ask the children to note the pattern of symmetry in the table and the reasons for it.
- Then they could find out whether the results are the same for a 3 x 5 and a 5 x 3 rectangle.

Display

- Display a series of rectangles and ask the children to identify any patterns. For example:

1 x 3

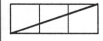

2 x 6

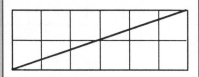

3 x 9

Activities

- The rectangles should be shaded in the following ways:

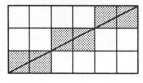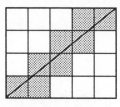

- Before asking the children to fill in the table, discuss ways of approaching the problem. For example, they could start by considering rectangles with a width of 1 unit:

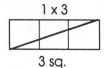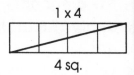

1 x 1	1 x 2	1 x 3	1 x 4
1 sq.	2 sq.	3 sq.	4 sq.

They should then move on to rectangles with a width of 2 units:

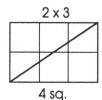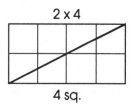

2 x 1	2 x 2	2 x 3	2 x 4
2 sq.	2 sq.	4 sq.	4 sq.

The pattern that develops is shown in the second row of this table. The completed table is shown below.

Length of rectangle

	1	2	3	4	5	6	7	8
1	1	2	3	4	5	6	7	8
2	2	2	4	4	6	6	8	8
3	3	4	3	6	7	6	9	10
4	4	4	6	4	8	8	10	10
5	5	6	7	8	5	10	11	12
6	6	6	6	8	10	6	12	12
7	7	8	9	10	11	12	7	14
8	8	8	10	10	12	12	14	8

Width of rectangle

36   IDEAS BANK – *Mathematics: Pattern*   © Folens

Diagonal Patterns

- The diagonal of this 6 x 8 rectangle runs through twelve squares:

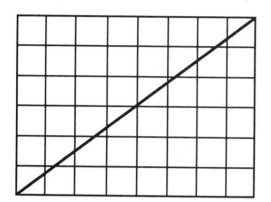

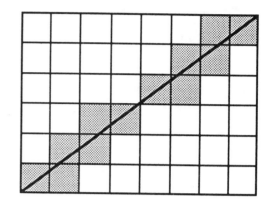

- Draw the diagonals on these rectangles.
- Shade the squares through which the diagonal passes, and count them.

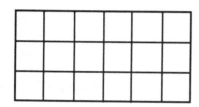

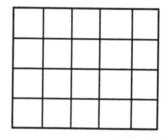

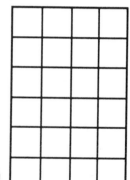

- Record each number in the table.

Length of rectangle

		1	2	3	4	5	6	7	8
Width of rectangle	1								
	2								
	3								
	4								
	5								
	6								12
	7								
	8								

- Use squared paper to draw more rectangles.
- Draw their diagonals and count the number of squares through which they pass.
- Record the results in the table.
- Complete the table and look for patterns.

Circle Patterns - Ideas Page

Aim

- To search for relationships between the number of lines, regions and intersections created by a fixed number of points plotted on the circumference of a circle.

Extension

- The children could experiment to find out how many lines can be drawn from each spot. Explain that this is one less than the number of spots on the circle.

Activities

- The completed table is:

Number of spots	Number of lines	Number of regions	Number of intersections
2	1	2	0
3	3	4	0
4	6	8	1
5	10	16	5
6	15	31	14

- Advise the children to count regions by writing a number in each one:

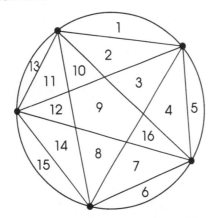

- Ask the children to identify the shapes of the regions within each circle. For example, the five-spot circle above consists of five sectors, ten triangles and one pentagon.
- Encourage the children to investigate the pattern in the number of lines column. They could find out if it is possible to predict the number of lines for circles with more than six spots (these are triangular numbers).

Display

- Ask the children to investigate the number of regions that can be created by drawing the same number of chords on circles in different ways. For example, three chords could be drawn to form the following numbers of regions:

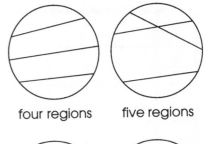

four regions   five regions

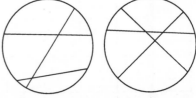

six regions   seven regions

- Display the drawings in the classroom.

Circle Patterns

- Draw a line from each spot to every other spot in each circle.
- Then count:
  - the number of lines you have drawn
  - the number of regions inside the circle
  - the number of intersections.

One has been done for you.
- Write your answers in the table.

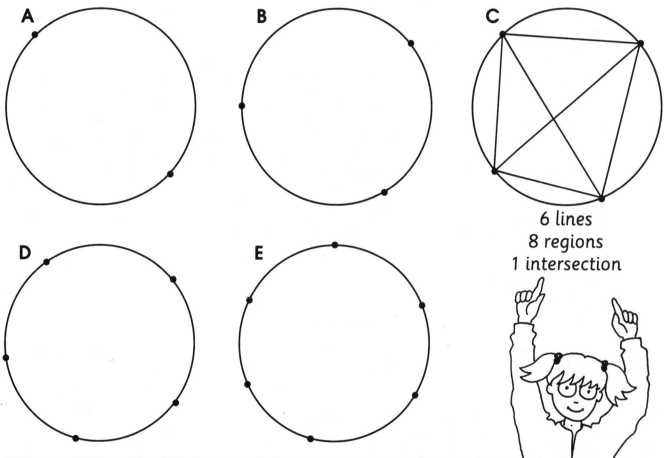

C

6 lines
8 regions
1 intersection

	Number of spots	Number of lines	Number of regions	Number of intersections
A	2			
B	3			
C	4	6	8	1
D	5			
E	6			

- Can you identify any patterns?

Calculator Patterns - Ideas Page

Aim

- To search for patterns in the number of light bars required to show digits on a calculator display.

Extension

- The children could find out how many light bars are required to show three-digit numbers.
- Ask them to examine the display of a digital watch or clock and to work out how many light bars would be needed to show certain times.
- The children could pretend that one of the light bars does not work. Set them problems. For example, if the middle bar is faulty, which numbers will look the same on the display? One answer is 0 and 8.

Activities

- The number of shaded light bars required to show the single digits are:

Digit	0	1	2	3	4	5	6	7	8	9
Light bars	6	2	5	5	4	5	6	4	7	6

- 8 requires the most light bars and 1 the least.
- The two-digit numbers are shown by the following numbers of light bars:

Digit	36	27	51	80
Light bars	11	9	7	13

- Ask the children to identify the two-digit number requiring:
  - the fewest shaded light bars (11 – 4 light bars)
  - the most shaded light bars (88 – 14 light bars).
- Encourage the children to devise a method for solving the problem. For example, if the total number of light bars is eight, then the digits could be made up of 2 and 6 light bars, or 3 and 5 light bars, or 4 and 4 light bars. The numbers which can be shown by:
  - 2 and 6 light bars are 10, 16, 19, 61, 91
  - 3 and 5 light bars are none, as no single digit number can be made with 3 light bars
  - 4 and 4 light bars are 44, 47, 74.

Display

- Ask the children to construct a table to show the numbers that require a given number of light bars.

Number of light bars		Total
4		
5		
6		
7		
8	10, 16, 19, 44, 47, 61, 74, 91	8
9		
10		
11		
12		
13		
14		

Calculator Patterns

- Shade the light bars to show each calculator number.
  One has been done for you.

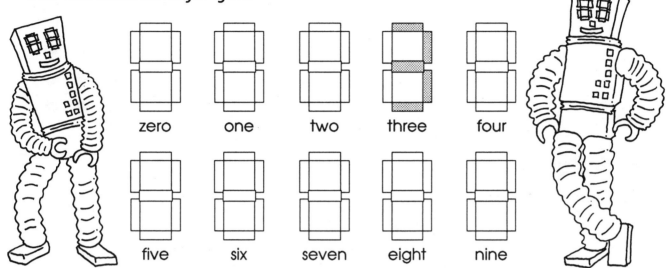

zero   one   two   three   four

five   six   seven   eight   nine

- How many light bars need to be shaded to show each number?
- Which number uses:
  - the most light bars ?
  - the fewest light bars?
- Shade these two-digit numbers.
  Write the number of light bars that have been shaded.

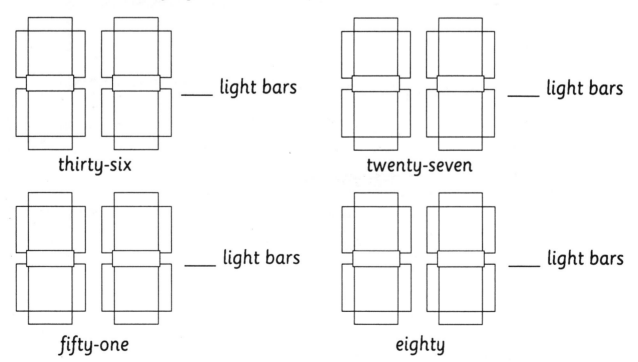

_____ light bars

thirty-six

_____ light bars

twenty-seven

_____ light bars

fifty-one

_____ light bars

eighty

- How many two-digit numbers can you find
  that use eight light bars?

Aims

- To add sequences of odd numbers and identify any patterns that result.
- To describe patterns.
- To recognise square numbers.

Extension

- Develop the activity by asking the children to add four consecutive odd numbers:

  $1 + 3 + 5 + 7 = 16$
  $3 + 5 + 7 + 9 = 24$

  These will all be multiples of 8.
- They could then move on to add five consecutive odd numbers:

  $1 + 3 + 5 + 7 + 9 = 25$
  $3 + 5 + 7 + 9 + 11 = 35$

  The answers are the multiples of 5 that are not multiples of 10.
- Ask the children to add consecutive even numbers in a similar way and to identify any patterns.

Activities

- The answers for the first section are all square numbers. The total of the first five odd numbers is the fifth square number.

  $1 + 3 = 4$
  $1 + 3 + 5 = 9$
  $1 + 3 + 5 + 7 = 16$

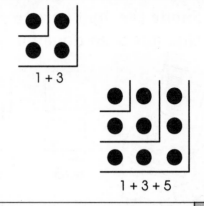

1 + 3

1 + 3 + 5

- The pattern could be illustrated using counters or a pegboard.
- When pairs of consecutive numbers are added in sequence, the following pattern results:

$1 + 3 = 4$	$5 + 7 = 12$
$3 + 5 = 8$	$7 + 9 = 16$

  These are all multiples of 4.
- Point out that the total of each sum is twice the even number that falls between the two odd numbers that are being added.
- When three consecutive odd numbers are added the totals are all the odd multiples of 3:

$1 + 3 + 5 = 9$	$5 + 7 + 9 = 21$
$3 + 5 + 7 = 15$	$7 + 9 + 11 = 27$

- Explain that the total of any three consecutive odd numbers is three times the middle number.

Display

- The patterns could be illustrated and displayed by using sticky circles. For example, these displays show that the sum of three consecutive odd numbers is always a multiple of 3.

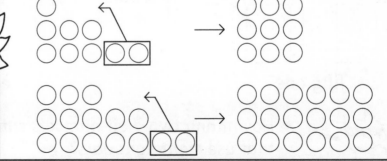

Odd Number Patterns

- Some odd numbers are:

1 3 5 7 9 11 13 15 17

Adding odd numbers

- Add the first two: 1 + 3 = _____

- Add the first three: 1 + 3 + 5 = _____

- Add more odd numbers in this way.
- Do you notice any pattern?

Adding two consecutive odd numbers

3 + 5 = _____

11 + 13 = _____

- Add more pairs of consecutive odd numbers.
- Do you notice any patterns?

Adding three consecutive odd numbers

3 + 5 + 7 = _____

11 + 13 + 15 = _____

- Add more sets of three consecutive odd numbers.
- Do you notice any patterns?

Calendar Patterns - Ideas Page

Aims

- To identify and describe patterns formed by the position of numbers in a calendar month.
- To practise adding two or three numbers from the calendar.

Display

- Obtain a calendar and highlight different number patterns.

October

M	Tu	W	Th	F	Sa	Su
			1	2	3	4
5	6	7	8	9	10	11
12	13	14	15	16	17	18
19	20	21	22	23	24	25
26	27	28	29	30	31	

Activities

- The diagonals from bottom left to top right form a sequence that descends in sixes.
- The diagonals from top left to bottom right form a sequence that ascends in eights.
- Some examples of 2 x 2 squares are:

6	7
13	14

2	3
9	10

15	16
22	23

- Point out that in each square:
  - the row totals differ by fourteen (two weeks)
  - the column totals differ by two (two days)
  - the diagonal totals are the same.

Extension

- The children could find out whether the same patterns apply to other months. Suggest they start by looking at the current month in detail.
- Ask them to investigate the properties of 3 x 3 squares from a page of a calendar and to identify any patterns formed by the row, column and diagonal totals.
- When the children have fully explored calendar patterns, introduce a more challenging activity:
  - Ask the children to imagine any of the calendar months.
  - Tell them that today is Wednesday the 10th. Ask them to imagine the position of 10 on 'their' calendar.
  - Ask them the following series of questions.

1. What is the number below, above, to the left, and to the right of 10?
2. What are the other numbers in the column?
3. What are the other numbers in the row?
4. What is the first day of the month?
5. What is the last day of the month?
6. What is the date a week on Monday?
7. What was the date last Sunday?

Calendar Patterns

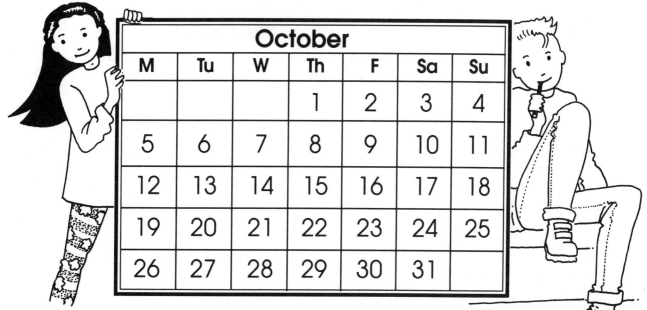

October

M	Tu	W	Th	F	Sa	Su
			1	2	3	4
5	6	7	8	9	10	11
12	13	14	15	16	17	18
19	20	21	22	23	24	25
26	27	28	29	30	31	

- Write numbers from the diagonals of the calendar in these boxes. One has been done for you.

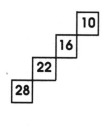 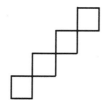 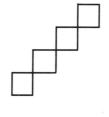

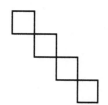 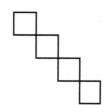 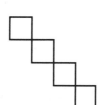

- Describe any patterns you notice.

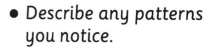
_____
_____
_____
_____

- Copy some 2 x 2 squares from the calendar.
- One has been done for you.

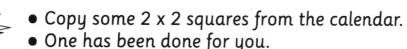

5	6
12	13

- Describe any patterns you notice.
_____
_____
_____

Flower Bed Patterns - Ideas Page

Aims

- To construct different-sized rectangles using a set of squares.
- To recognise the dimensions of the inner and outer rectangles that are created.

Activities

- The children could use sets of squares or interlocking cubes to build the gardens.
- The answers for the first section are:

Size of garden	4 x 5	3 x 4	3 x 3	7 x 4
Size of flower bed	2 x 3	1 x 2	1 x 1	5 x 2
Number of paving stones	14	10	8	18

- The children could draw and complete a table to show the number of gardens that can be built from up to 15 paving stones.

number of stones	size of garden	size of flower bed	picture
8	3 x 3	1 x 1 (1sq)	
10	3 x 4	1 x 2 (2sq)	
12	3 x 5 4 x 4	1 x 3 (3sq) 2 x 2 (4sq)	
14	3 x 6 4 x 5	1 x 4 (4sq) 2 x 3 (6sq)	

Extension

- Ask the children to construct different-sized flower beds and to investigate how many paving stones are needed.
- Encourage them to describe the relationship between:
  - The dimensions of the garden and the flower bed. For example, a garden 4 x 3 has a flower bed 2 x 1; a garden 5 x 3 has a flower bed 3 x 1. Therefore, the dimensions of the flower beds are two less than the dimensions of the garden.
  - The number of stones and the dimensions of the flower bed. Focus on the perimeters of the rectangles. For example, a flower bed 2 x 3 has 2 + 2 + 3 + 3 + 4 = 14 stones. The number of stones is the perimeter plus 4 for the corners.

Display

- Display a large chart on the wall to represent the number of paving stones for different-sized gardens.
- The children could complete the entries as they find them.
- They could search for patterns in the completed chart.

Flower Bed Patterns

- The white squares are paving stones which surround a flower bed in a garden.
- The shaded area is the flower bed.
- For each of these gardens, write:
  - the length and width of the garden
  - the length and width of the flower bed
  - the number of paving stones around the outside of the flower bed.

Size of garden: _____
Size of flower bed: _____
Number of paving stones: _____

Size of garden: **3 x 4**
Size of flower bed: **1 x 2**
Number of paving stones: **10**

Size of garden: _____
Size of flower bed: _____
Number of paving stones: _____

Size of garden: _____
Size of flower bed: _____
Number of paving stones: _____

- How many different gardens can you make using up to 15 paving stones?
- Which garden has the largest flower bed?

- How many different gardens can you make using 20 paving stones?
- Which garden has the largest flower bed?

Eight ways to help ...

There are hundreds of ideas in this book to enable you to develop and extend the photocopiable pages. Here are just eight ways to help you make the most of the **Ideas Bank** series.

1 Photocopy a page, paste it on to card and laminate or cover it with sticky-backed plastic to use with groups. Children can now write on the pages using water-based pens and this can be washed off.

2 Photocopy on to both sides of the paper. Put another useful activity on the back. Develop a simple filing system so others can find relevant sheets and do not duplicate them again.

7 Make an overhead transparency of the page. You and your colleagues can now use the idea time and time again.

3 Save the sheets – if the children do not have to cut them up as a part of the activity – and re-use. Label the sets, and keep them safely in files.

8 Ask yourself: "Does every child in this class/group need to deal with/work through this photocopiable sheet?"
If not, don't photocopy it!

4 Make the most of group work. Children working in small groups need only one sheet to discuss between them.

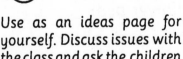

6 Use as an ideas page for yourself. Discuss issues with the class and ask the children to produce artwork and writing.

5 Put the sheets inside clear plastic wallets. This means the sheets are easily stored in a binder and will last longer. Children's writing can again be wiped away.